ASPEN COMICS PRESENTS

VOLUME ONE: HORSEMEN

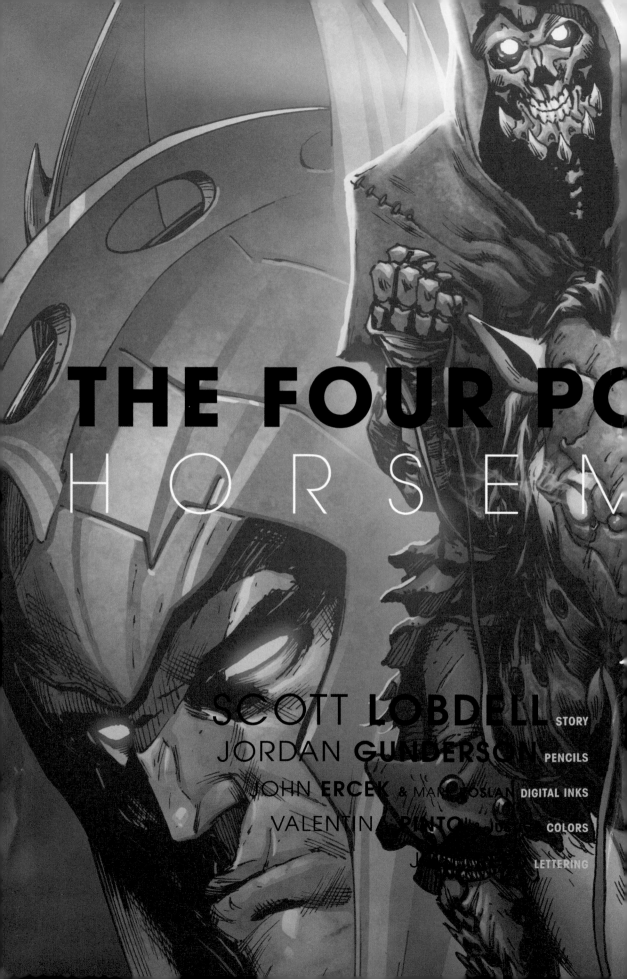

THE FOUR PO

HORSEM

SCOTT LOBDELL STORY

JORDAN GUNDERSON PENCILS

JOHN ERCEK & MAR ... OSLAN DIGITAL INKS

VALENTIN ... PINTO ... COLORS

... LETTERING

SCOTT LOBDELL

GIA SORENTINO, IVANA GHOUL AND ARA **CREATED BY SCOTT LOBDELL**
ASPEN MATTHEWS **CREATED BY MICHAEL TURNER**

HE FOUR POINTS™ VOLUME I: HORSEMEN
SBN: 978-1-941511-10-7 FIRST PRINTING, REGULAR EDITION 2016. Collects material originally published as The Four Points 1-5
ISBN: 978-1-941511-11-4 FIRST PRINTING, COMIC BENTO VARIANT EDITION 2016. Collects material originally published as The Four Points 1-5

Published by Aspen MLT, Inc.
Office of Publication: 5701 W. Slauson Ave. Suite. 120, Culver City, CA 90230.

Address correspondence to:

THE FOUR POINTS c/o Aspen MLT Inc.
5701 W. Slauson Ave. Suite. 120
Culver City, CA. 90230-6946
or fanmail@aspencomics.com

Visit us on the web at:
aspencomics.com
aspenstore.com
facebook.com/aspencomics
twitter.com/aspencomics

ORIGINAL SERIES EDITORS:
VINCE HERNANDEZ AND **FRANK MASTROMAURO**
ASSISTANT EDITORS: **ANDREA SHEA, JOSH REED** AND **GABE CARRASCO**

FOR THIS EDITION:
SUPERVISING EDITOR: **FRANK MASTROMAURO**
EDITORS: **VINCE HERNANDEZ** AND **GABE CARRASCO**
COVER DESIGN: **MARK ROSLAN**
BOOK DESIGN AND PRODUCTION: **MARK ROSLAN**
LOGO DESIGN: **PETER STEIGERWALD**
COVER ILLUSTRATION: **JORDAN GUNDERSON** AND **VALENTINA PINTO**

FOR ASPEN:
FOUNDER: MICHAEL TURNER
CO-OWNER: PETER STEIGERWALD
CO-OWNER/PRESIDENT: FRANK MASTROMAURO
VICE PRESIDENT/EDITOR IN CHIEF: VINCE HERNANDEZ
VICE PRESIDENT/DESIGN AND PRODUCTION: MARK ROSLAN
EDITORIAL ASSISTANTS: GABE CARRASCO AND JOSH REED
PRODUCTION ASSISTANT: CHAZ RIGGS
OFFICE COORDINATOR: MEGAN MADRIGAL
ASPENSTORE.COM: CHRIS RUPP

To find the Comic Shop nearest you...

888-COMIC-BOOK
csls.diamondcomics.com
1-888-266-4226

CHAPTER ONE
"POINT OF ENTRY"

COVER A TO
THE FOUR POINTS #1 by
• JORDAN **GUNDERSON** • VALENTINA **PINTO** •

SEVERAL DOZEN VICTIMS WERE "MELTED" TOGETHER IN A WRITHING HEAP, HALF A WORLD APART.

THE FOUR OF US NEED TO FIND THE CAUSE OF THIS AND STOP IT.

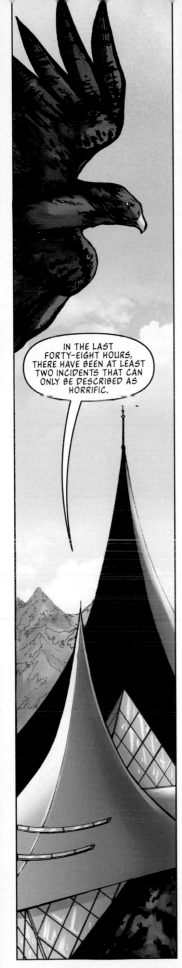

IN THE LAST FORTY-EIGHT HOURS, THERE HAVE BEEN AT LEAST TWO INCIDENTS THAT CAN ONLY BE DESCRIBED AS HORRIFIC.

I DO NOT MEAN TO BE RUDE.

BUT FOR THE MOMENT THERE ARE ONLY THREE OF US.

TRADITIONALLY, THERE ARE FOUR HORSEMEN OF THE APOCALYPSE...POWERFUL ENTITIES DETERMINED TO DESTROY THE WORLD.

BUT IN THEIR WAY, THERE HAVE ALWAYS BEEN FOUR ELEMENTS--THAT, WHEN BROUGHT TOGETHER--ARE AN UNSTOPPABLE FORCE FOR GOOD.

EARTH, WIND, FIRE...

CHAPTER TWO

"WATER SEEKS ITS
OWN LEVEL"

COVER A TO
THE FOUR POINTS #2 by
• JORDAN **GUNDERSON** • JUAN **FERNANDEZ** •

DR. MATTHEWS. MY NAME IS GIA SORENTINO. I'VE COME TO ENLIST YOUR HELP WITH A VERY SERIOUS MATTER.

YOU CAN STOP RIGHT THERE. AFTER EVERYTHING THAT'S HAPPENED TO ME OVER THE PAST FEW MONTHS--

--I'VE LESS THAN ZERO INTEREST IN GETTING INVOLVED WITH WHATEVER ADVENTURE YOU INTEND TO DRAG ME INTO.

THANK YOU, BUT NO.

IT'S ALMOST CUTE THAT YOU THINK YOU HAVE A SAY IN THE MATTER.

THE TRUTH I AM ABOUT TO REVEAL TO YOU IS WAY CRAZIER THAN ANYTHING YOU--

MY FAULT. I'M NOT BEING CLEAR.

REALLY. NOT INTERESTED. AT ALL.

GOOD-BYE.

I TOTALLY UNDERSTAND. SAVING THE WORLD ISN'T FOR EVERYONE.

BREEP BREEP

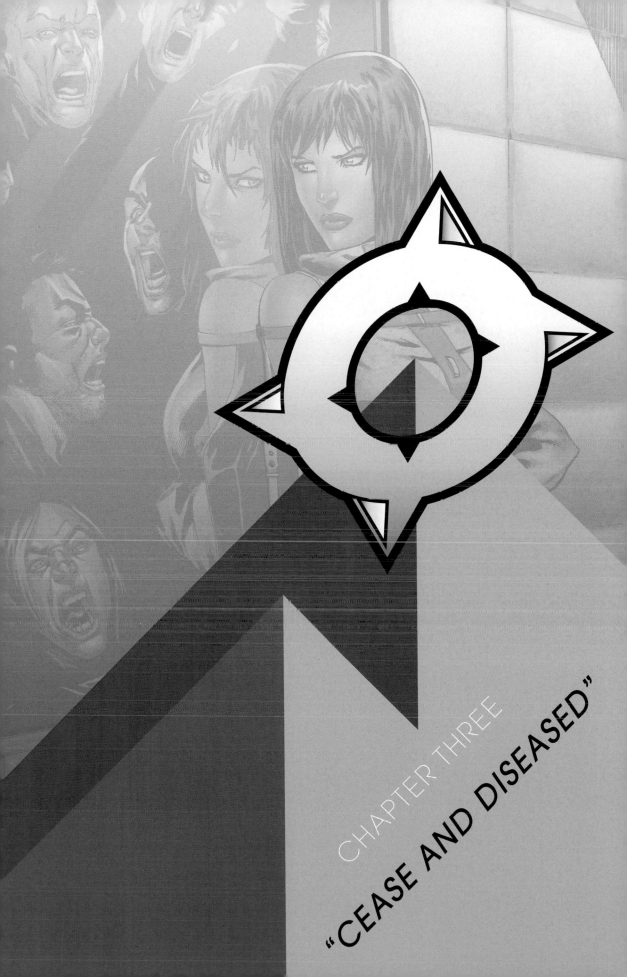

CHAPTER THREE

"CEASE AND DISEASED"

COVER A TO
THE FOUR POINTS #3 by
• JORDAN **GUNDERSON** • JUAN **FERNANDEZ** •

CHAPTER FOUR
"FEAST...FAMINE...
OR DEATH"

COVER A TO
THE FOUR POINTS #4 by
• TINA VALENTINO • Peter STEIGERWALD •

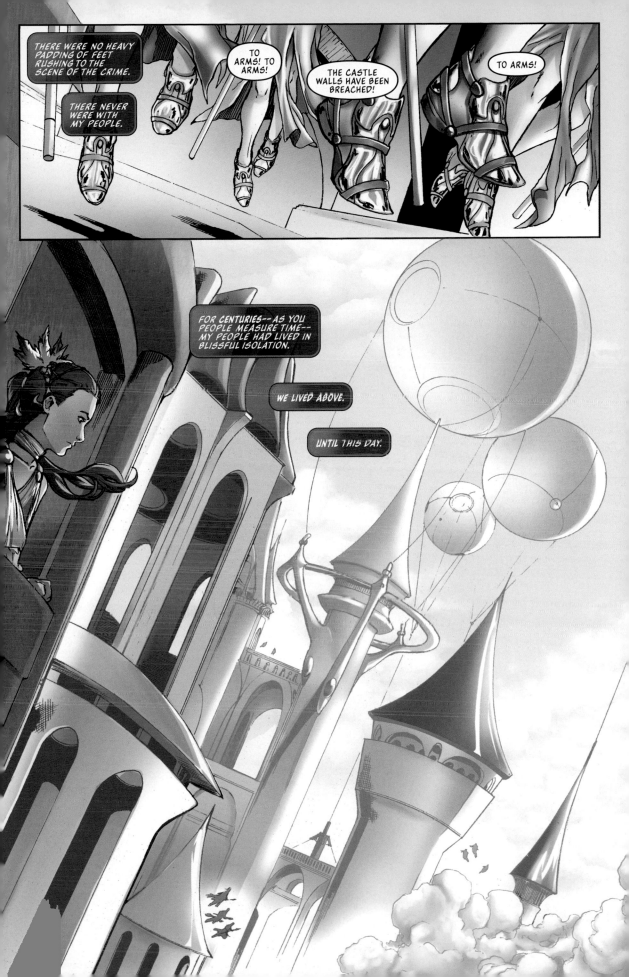

CHAPTER FIVE

"END POINTS"

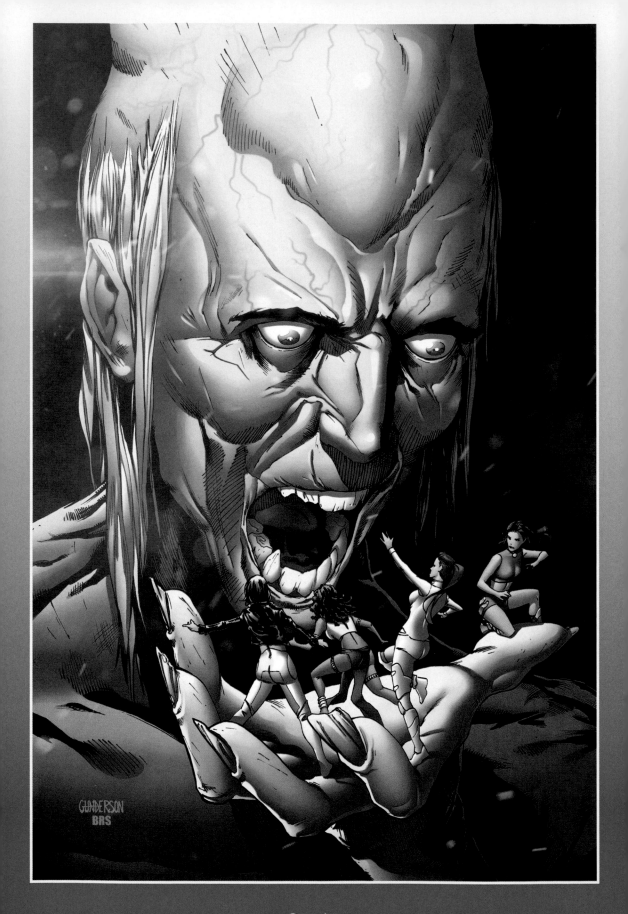

COVER A TO
THE FOUR POINTS #5 by
• Jordan **GUNDERSON** • Brett **SMITH** •

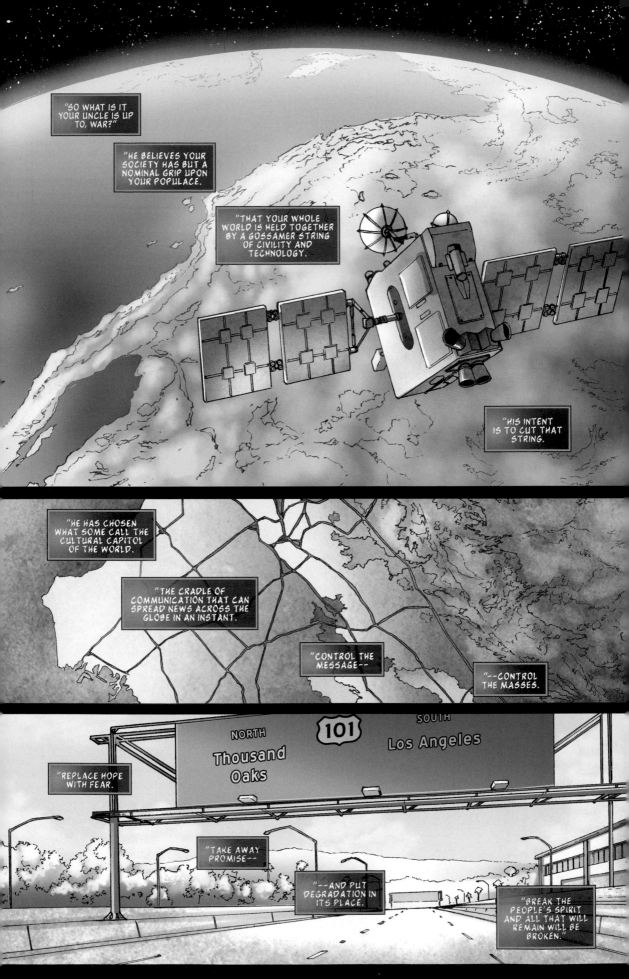

GIA, IVANA—I'M SORRY...

...BUT ARA IS GONE.

SHE *DROPKICKED* THAT MONSTER BEFORE SHE WENT.

HAS HIS *SPELL* GONE WITH HIM?

IT *MIGHT HAVE*, IVANA! A FEW MOMENTS AGO I COULDN'T REACH ANY OF THESE PEOPLE PSIONICALLY, BUT NOW—

—THEY ARE *WEAKENING!*

NO— *MORE* THAN THAT!

THEY'RE... *FREE?*

WOULD *SOMEONE* TELL ME WHAT JUST HAPPENED?

YES, MR. PRESIDENT.

WE JUST SAVED THE WORLD.

AT THE COST OF ONE OF OUR OWN.

PRETTY MUCH.

COVER GALLERY

COVER B TO
THE FOUR POINTS #1 by
• Khary **RANDOLPH** • Erick **ARCINIEGA** •

RETAILER INCENTIVE COVER C TO
THE FOUR POINTS #1 by
• JORDAN **GUNDERSON** • VALENTINA **PINTO** •

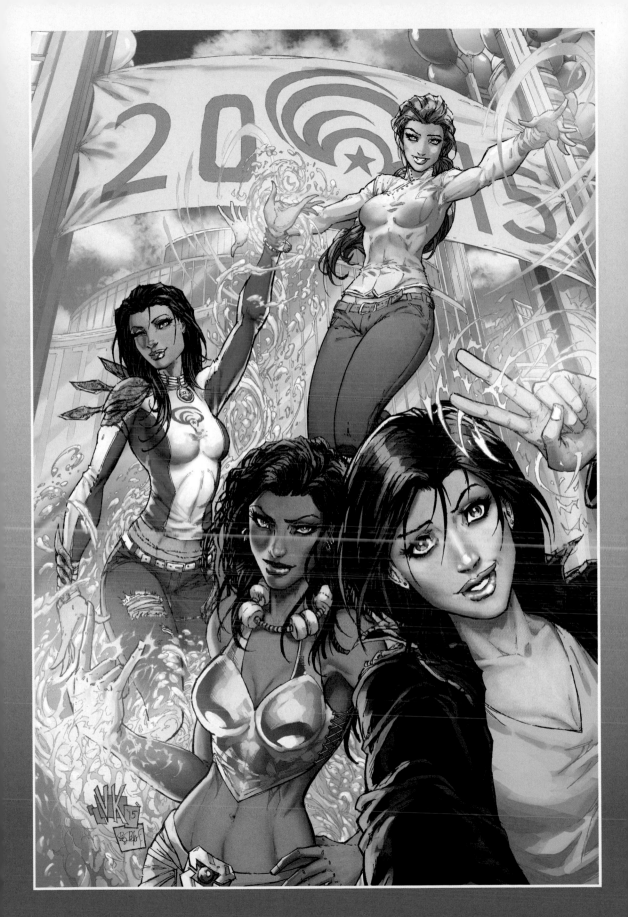

WonderCon Anaheim Convention Exclusive Cover F to
THE FOUR POINTS #1 by
• V Ken MARION • Mark ROSLAN • Peter STEIGERWALD •

COVER B TO
THE FOUR POINTS #2 by
• Khary **RANDOLPH** • Erick **ARCINIEGA** •

RETAILER INCENTIVE COVER C TO
THE FOUR POINTS #2 by
• JORDAN **GUNDERSON** • VALENTINA **PINTO** •

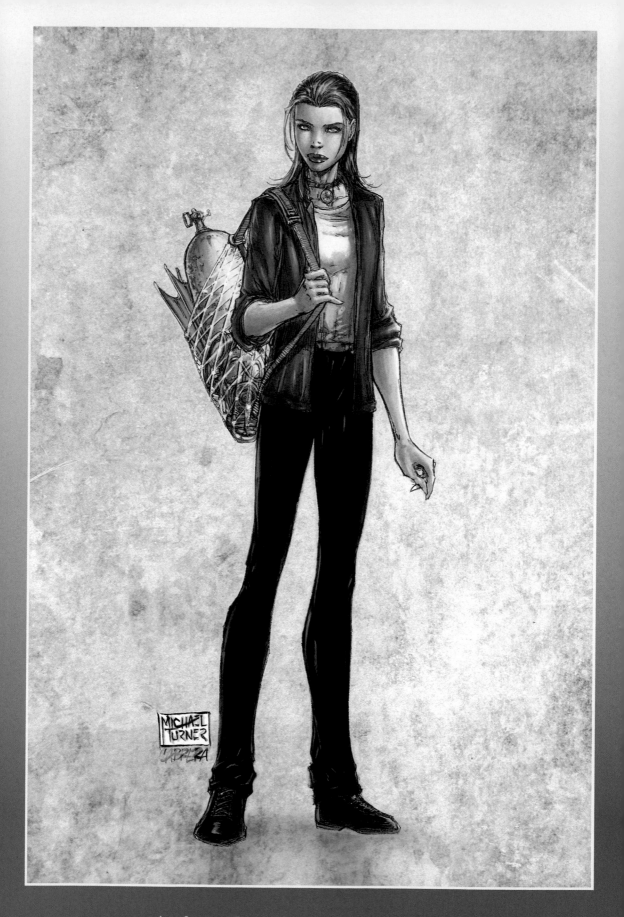

THE FOUR POINTS #2 by

• Michael **TURNER** • Nathan **CABRERA** •

ATLANTIC CITY BOARDWALK CON CONVENTION EXCLUSIVE COVER E to
THE FOUR POINTS #2 by
• JORDAN **GUNDERSON** • PETER **STEIGERWALD** •

COVER B TO
THE FOUR POINTS #3 by
• Khary **RANDOLPH** • Erick **ARCINIEGA** •

RETAILER INCENTIVE COVER C TO
THE FOUR POINTS #3 by
• JORDAN **GUNDERSON** • JUAN **FERNANDEZ** •

COVER B TO
THE FOUR POINTS #4 by
• TINA VALENTINO • PETER STEIGERWALD •

COVER C TO
THE FOUR POINTS #4 by
• TINA VALENTINO • Peter STEIGERWALD •

COVER D TO
THE FOUR POINTS #4 by
• TINA VALENTINO • PETER STEIGERWALD •

INTERLOCKING COVERS A, B, C, D to
THE FOUR POINTS #4
• TINA VALENTINO • PETER STEIGERWALD •

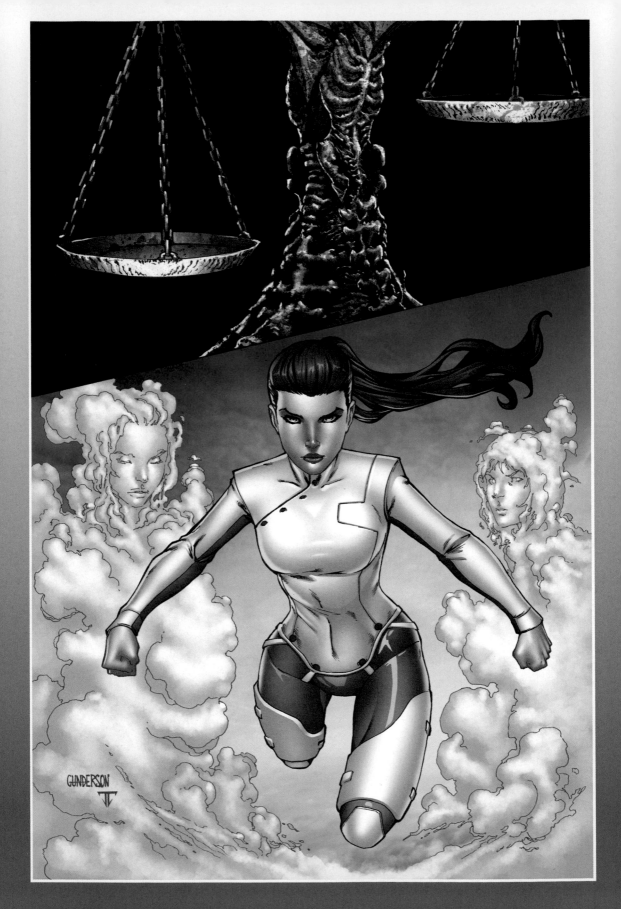

RETAILER INCENTIVE COVER E TO
THE FOUR POINTS #4 by
• JORDAN **GUNDERSON** • JUAN **FERNANDEZ** •

COVER B TO
THE FOUR POINTS #5 by
• KHARY RANDOLPH • ERICK ARCINIEGA •

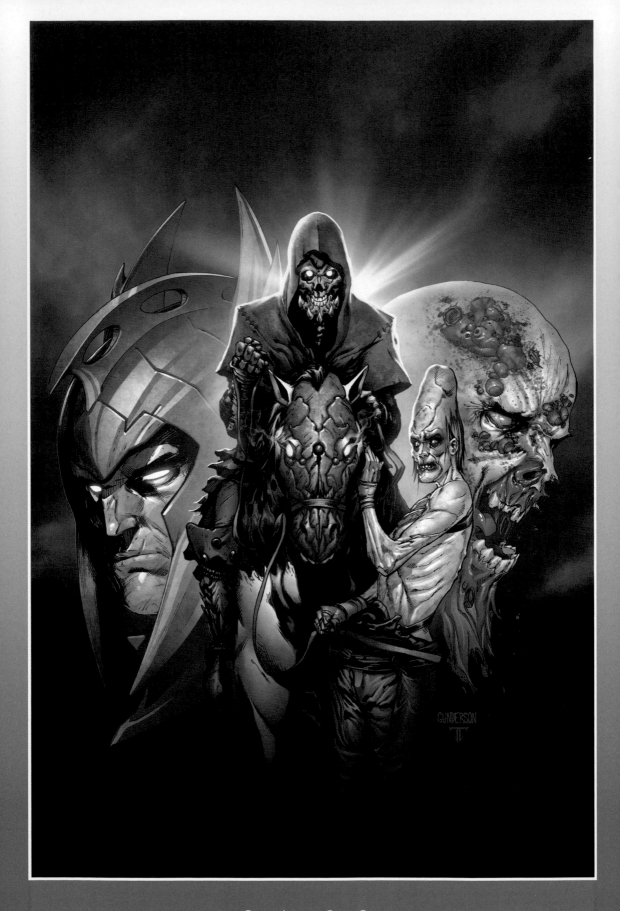

RETAILER INCENTIVE COVER C TO
THE FOUR POINTS #5 by
• JORDAN **GUNDERSON** • JUAN **FERNANDEZ** •

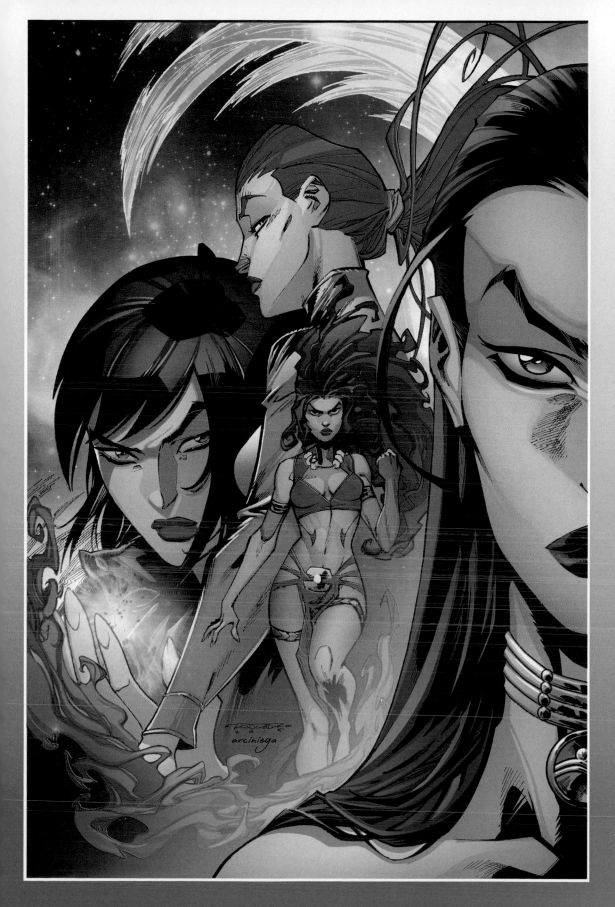

STAN LEE'S COMIKAZE CONVENTION EXCLUSIVE COVER D TO
THE FOUR POINTS #5 by
• KHARY **RANDOLPH** • ERICK **ARCINIEGA** •

MAORI TATS?

THE FOUR POINTS

CONCEPT SKETCHES
BY SERIES ARTIST
JORDAN GUNDERSON